ShowTime® Piano

Children's Songs

REVISED EDITION

Level 2A

Elementary Playing

This book belongs to: _____

D1279540

Arranged by

Nancy and Randall Faber

Production: Frank and Gail Hackinson
Production Coordinator: Philip Groeber
Cover: Terpstra Design, San Francisco
Engraving: Tempo Music Press, Inc.
Printer: Tempo Music Press, Inc.

THE
F·J·H
MUSIC
COMPANY
INC.
Frank J. Hackinson

2525 Davie Road, Suite 360
Fort Lauderdale, Florida 33317-7424

CHILDREN'S MUSIC TIME

Review these music symbols.

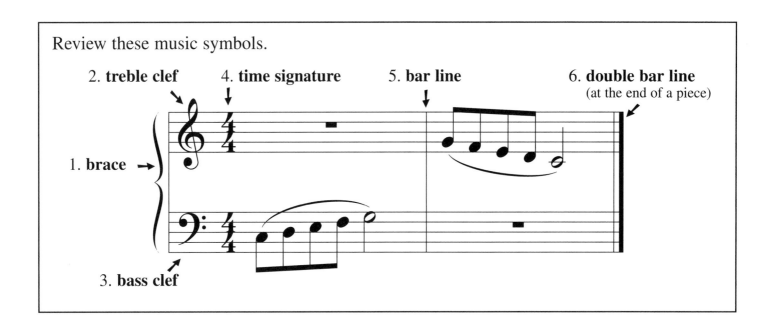

2. **treble clef**   4. **time signature**   5. **bar line**   6. **double bar line**
(at the end of a piece)

1. **brace**

3. **bass clef**

An Incomplete Song

Complete this song by adding each of the symbols
shown above (numbered 1–6). Your teacher may
help you. Then play the melody.

Cheerfully

This   is   my   book   of   songs.   It's   my   ver - y   own.

mf

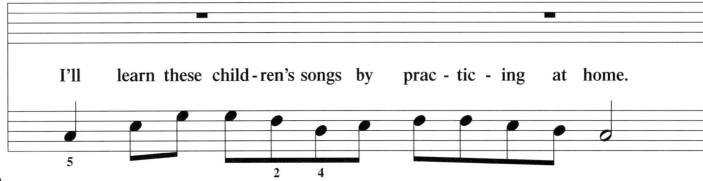

I'll   learn these chil-dren's songs   by   prac - tic - ing   at   home.

TABLE OF CONTENTS

Be Kind to Your Web-Footed Friends

TRADITIONAL

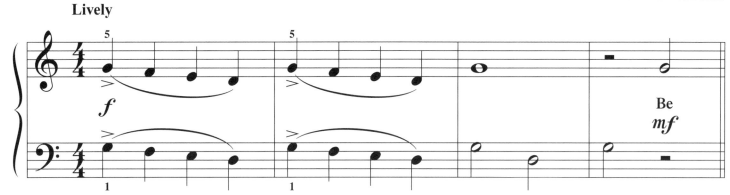

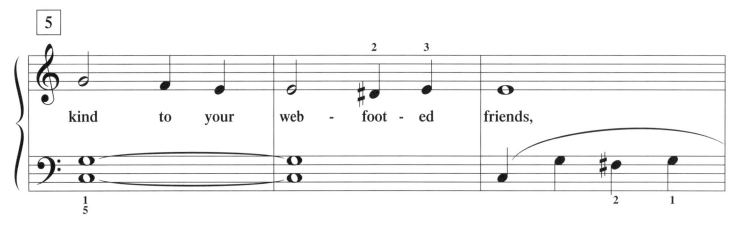

*Teacher's Note: For subsequent weeks of practice, the student may circle the stars or draw additional stars.

Teacher Duet: (Student plays 1 octave higher)

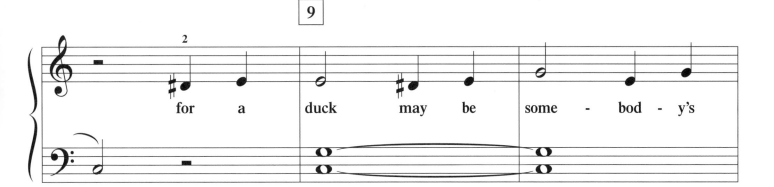

for a duck may be some - bod - y's

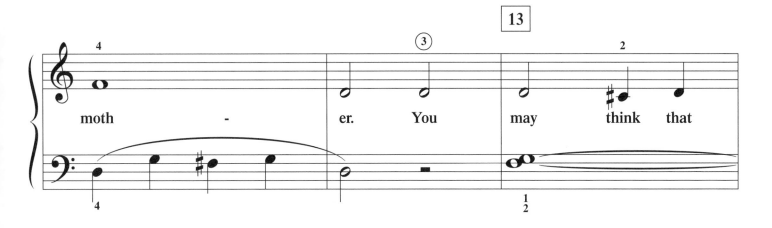

moth - er. You may think that

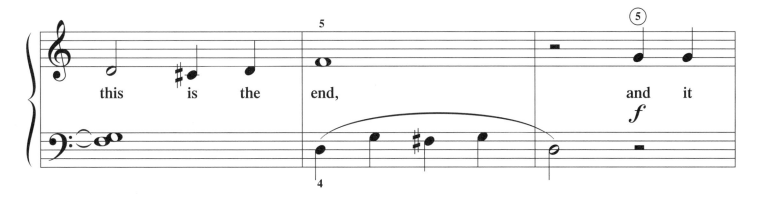

this is the end, and it

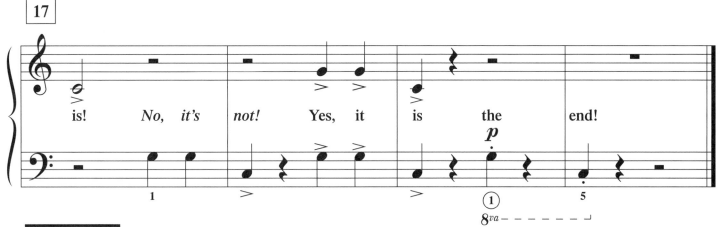

is! *No, it's not!* Yes, it is the end!

StudyTime

Point out the two places in the music where your hands are playing in **octaves** (8 notes apart).

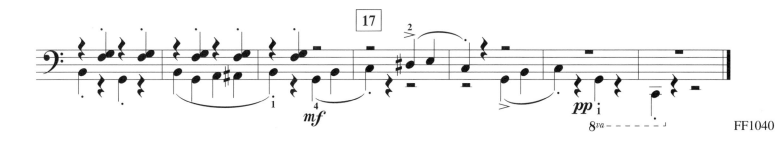

PRACTICE ____ TIMES DAILY.

Shade in a star for each day of practice.

Stewball

TRADITIONAL

Moderately

Old Stew - ball was a race - horse.

I wish he was mine.

Teacher Duet: (Student plays as written)

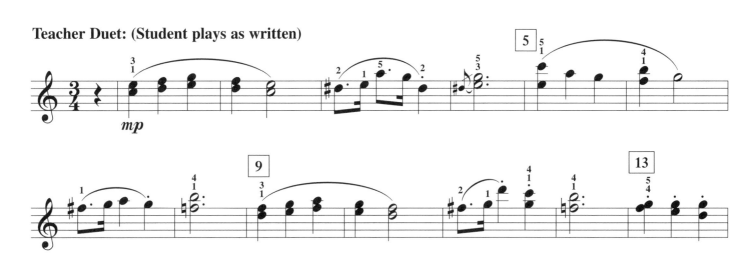

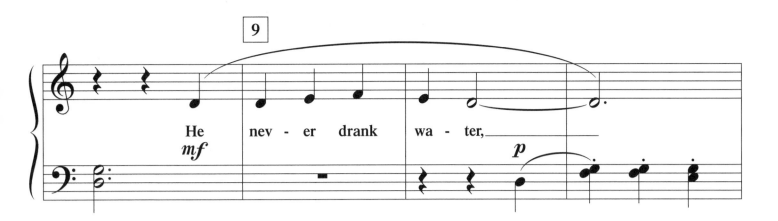

StudyTime

Your teacher will play *Stewball* and stop at any measure.
Follow the music and point to the measure where the music stops.

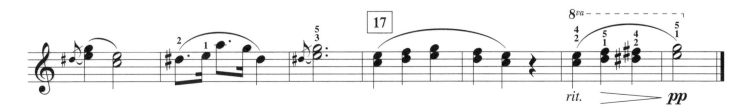

8

Shade in a star for each day of practice.

The Giant

Words by CRYSTAL BOWMAN
Music by NANCY FABER

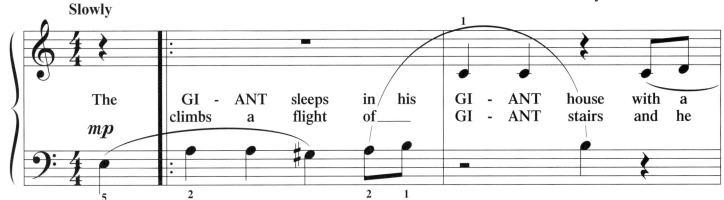

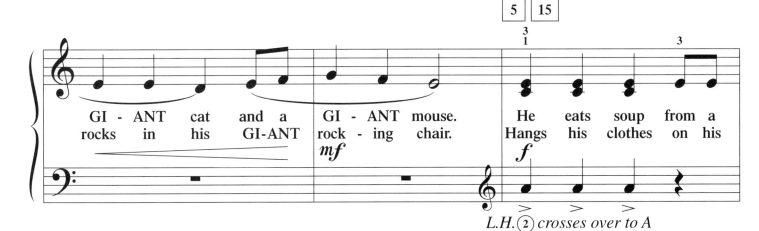

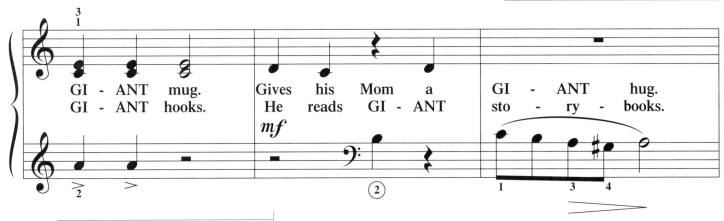

Teacher Duet: (Student plays 1 octave higher)

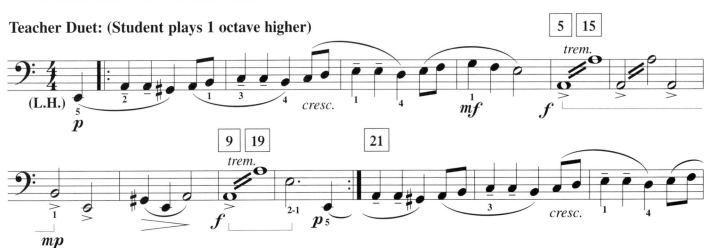

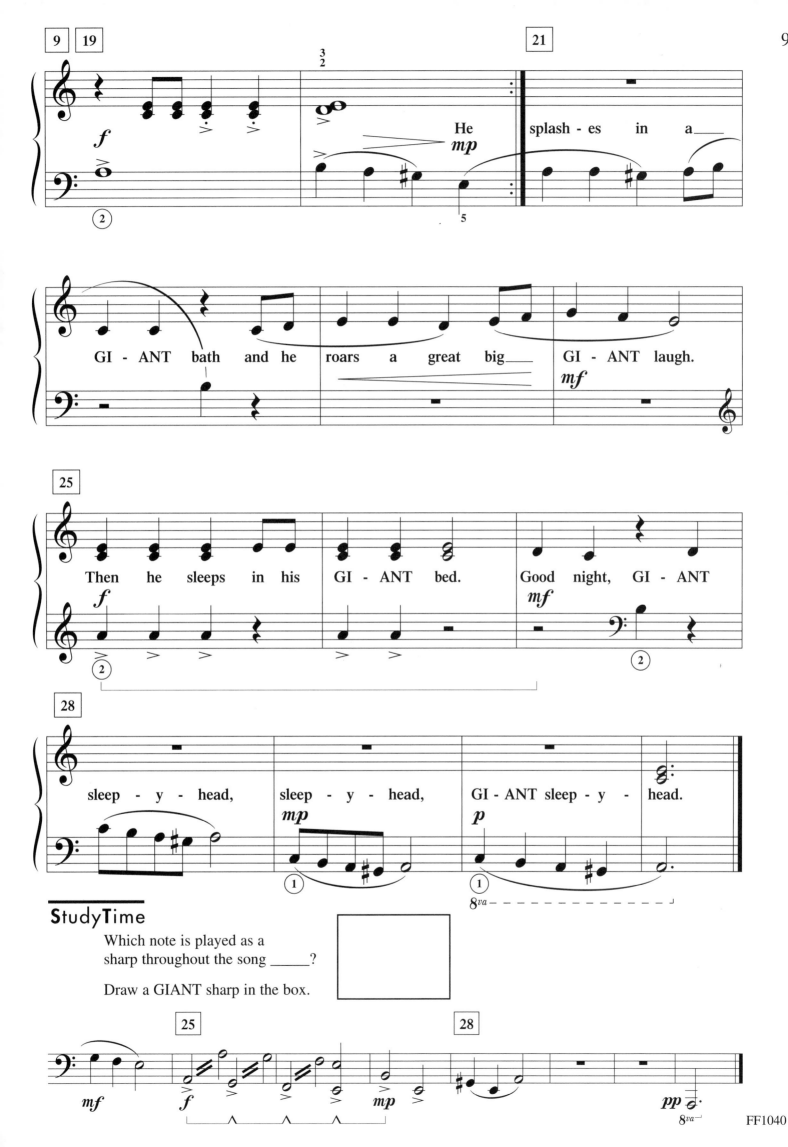

StudyTime

Which note is played as a
sharp throughout the song _____?

Draw a GIANT sharp in the box.

PRACTICE R.H. ALONE ____ TIMES DAILY.
PRACTICE H.T. ____ TIMES DAILY.

★ ★ ★ ★ ★ ★ ★

Shade in a star for each day of practice.

The Hokey Pokey

Words and Music by
**CHARLES P. MACAK, TAFFT BAKER,
and LARRY LaPRISE**

Moderately, with a swing*

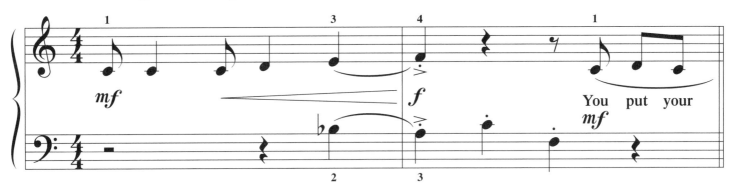

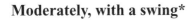

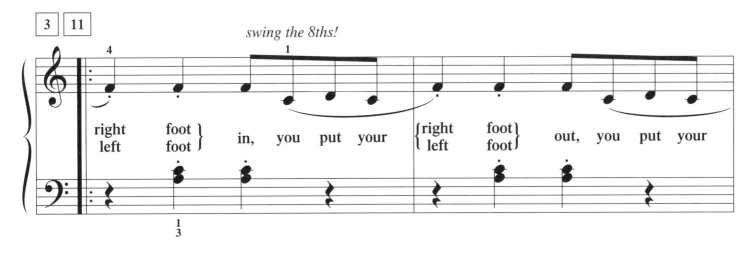

*Note to Teacher: ♫ should be played in a long-short pattern (♫ = ♩♪).

Teacher Duet: (Student plays 1 octave higher)

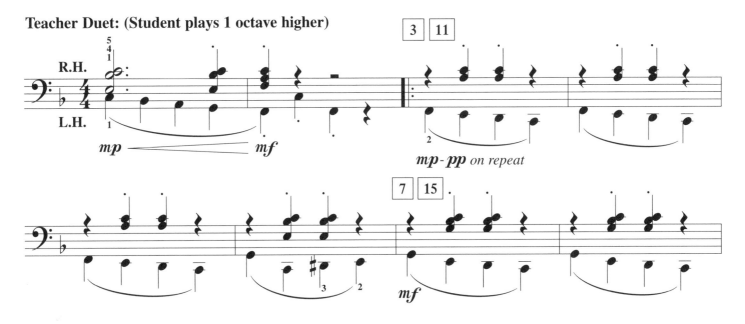

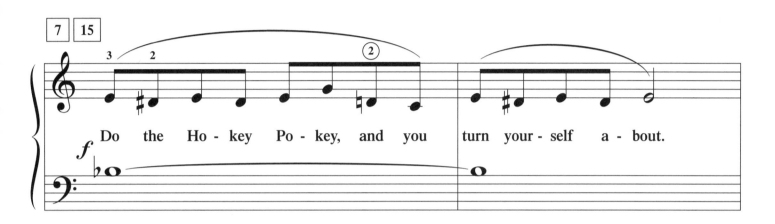

StudyTime

Point out these symbols in the music. Define each for your teacher:
slur, flat, staccato, accent, sharp, natural, crescendo.

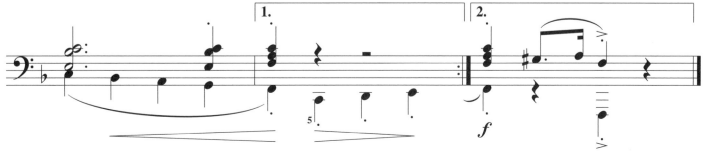

PRACTICE ____ TIMES DAILY AT A SLOW TEMPO.
PRACTICE ____ TIMES DAILY UP TO TEMPO.

⭐ ⭐ ⭐ ⭐ ⭐ ⭐ ⭐

Shade in a star for each day of practice.

Mail Myself to You

Words and Music by
WOODY GUTHRIE

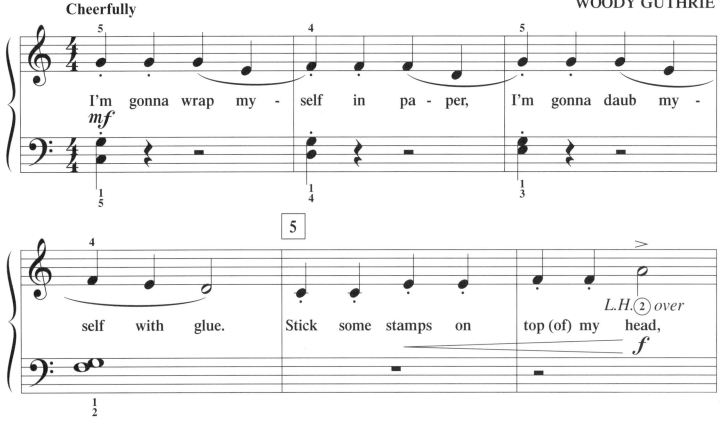

I'm gonna wrap my - self in pa - per, I'm gonna daub my -

self with glue. Stick some stamps on top (of) my head,

L.H. ② over

I'm gonna mail my - self to you. When you see me

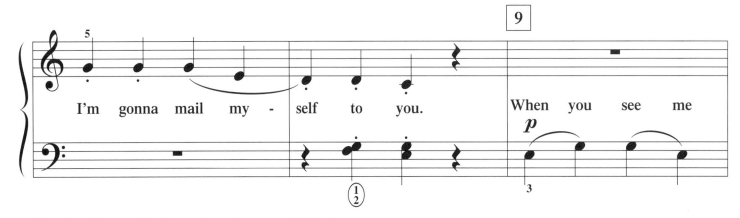

Teacher Duet: (Student plays 1 octave higher)

mp - pp on repeat

StudyTime

Put a ✓ above each measure that has the interval of a **3rd** (skip).

PRACTICE —— TIMES DAILY AT A SLOW TEMPO.
PRACTICE —— TIMES DAILY UP TO TEMPO.

★ ★ ★ ★ ★ ★ ★

Shade in a star for each day of practice.

What Do Witches Eat?

Lyrics by JENNIFER MacLEAN
Music by NANCY FABER

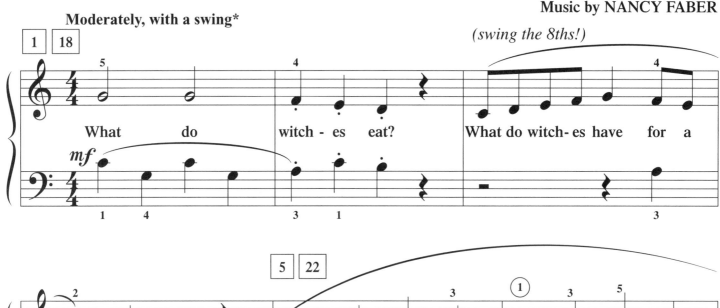

What do witch-es eat? What do witch-es have for a treat? Who knows? I've nev-er been asked to join their bunch when

*Note to Teacher: ♪♪ should be played in a long-short pattern (♪♪ = ♪ ♪).

Teacher Duet: (Student plays 1 octave higher)

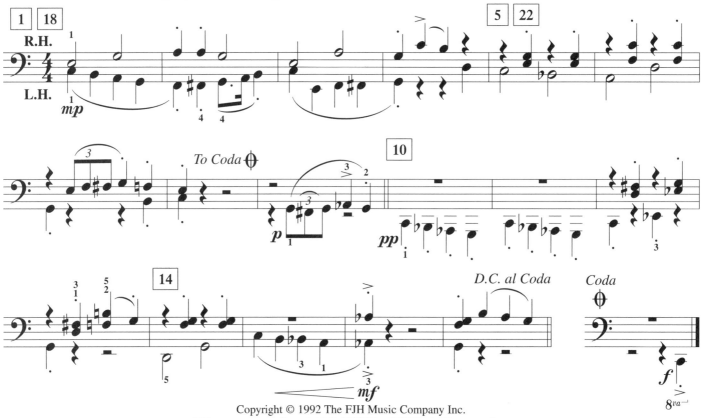

StudyTime

Circle three words below that match the rhythm of the **triplet**.

1. strawberry   4. jelly

2. popcorn   5. spookily

3. merrily   6. candy

16

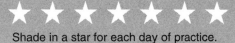

PRACTICE _____ TIMES DAILY AT A SLOW TEMPO.
PRACTICE _____ TIMES DAILY UP TO TEMPO.
★ ★ ★ ★ ★ ★ ★
Shade in a star for each day of practice.

Bling-Blang
(Build a House)

Words and Music by
WOODY GUTHRIE

Lively

You get a ham-mer, I'll get a nail, You catch a bird and
I'll grab some mud and you grab some clay, So when it rains it

I'll catch a snail. You bring a board and I'll bring a saw,
won't wash a-way. We'll build a house that'll be so___ strong,

Teacher Duet: (Student plays 1 octave higher)

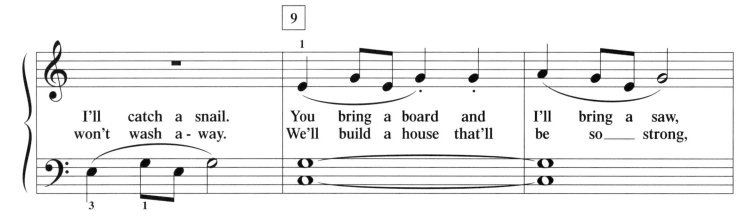

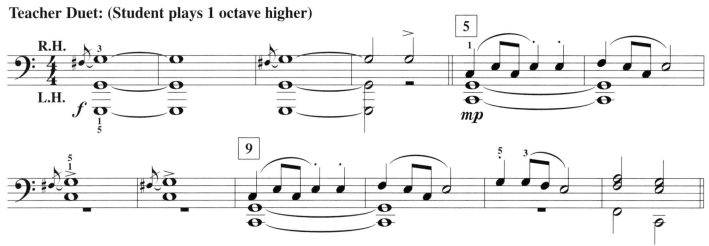

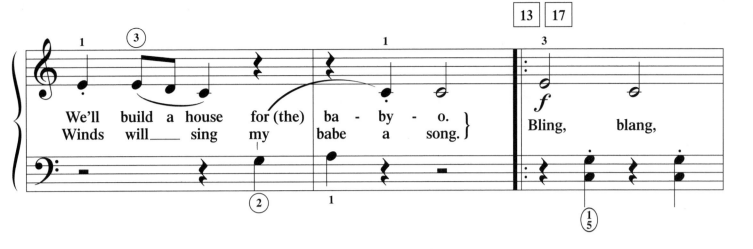

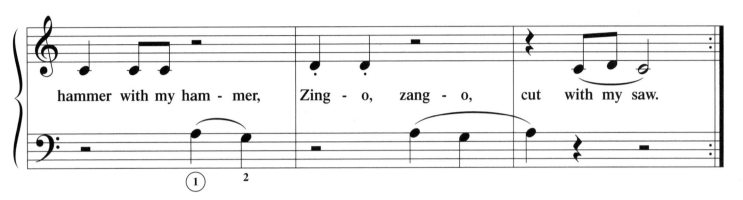

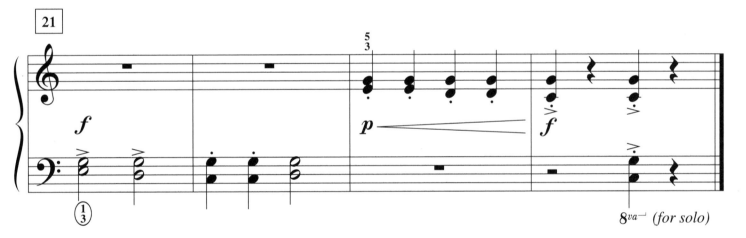

StudyTime

This song has an introduction and an ending.
Point out these sections to your teacher.

FF1040

PRACTICE R.H. ALONE ____ TIMES DAILY.
PRACTICE H.T. ____ TIMES DAILY.

Shade in a star for each day of practice.

All the Things in My Mind

Lyrics by JENNIFER MacLEAN
Music by NANCY FABER

Flowing gently

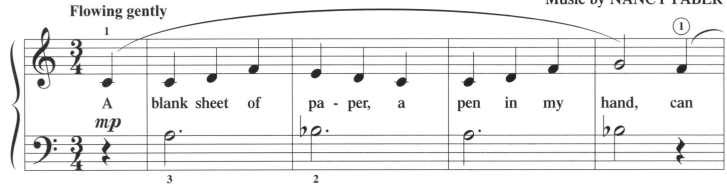

A blank sheet of pa-per, a pen in my hand, can

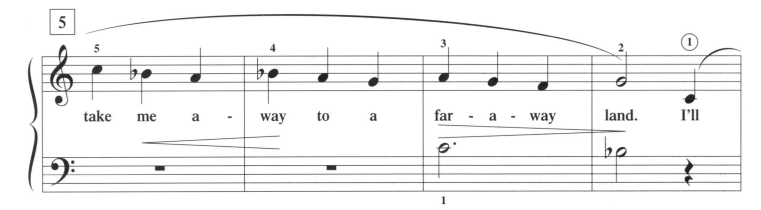

take me a - way to a far - a - way land. I'll

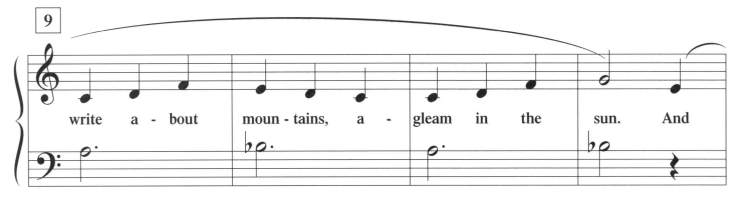

write a - bout moun - tains, a - gleam in the sun. And

Teacher Duet: (Student plays 1 octave higher)

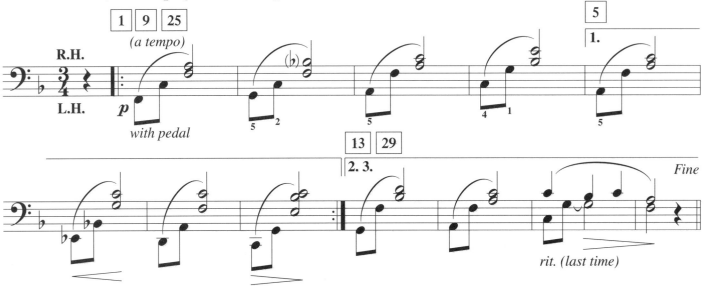

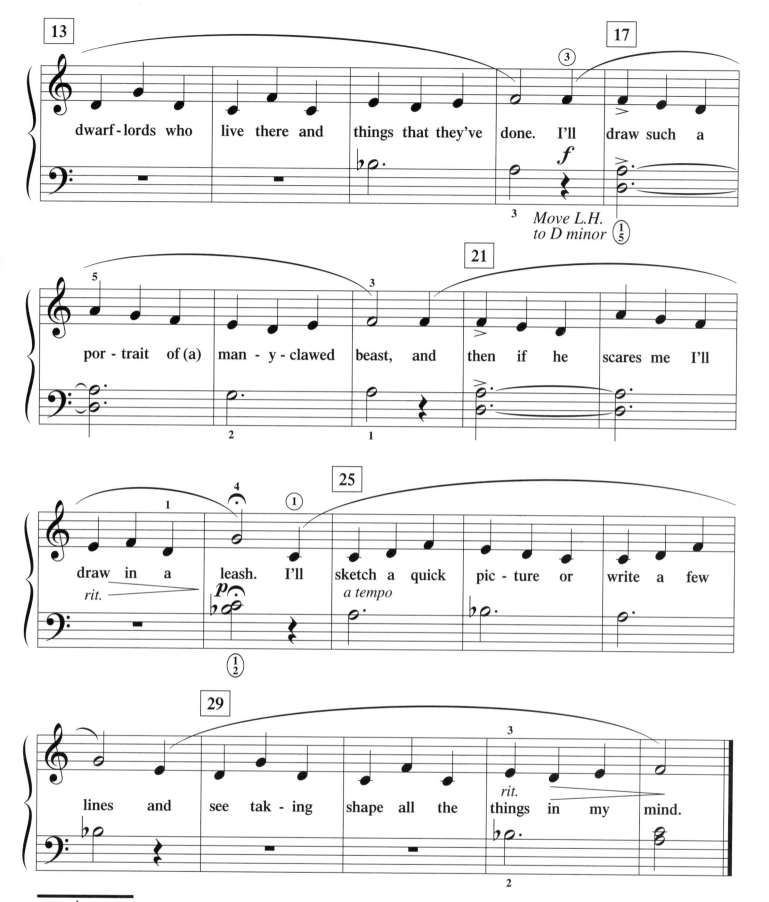

dwarf-lords who live there and things that they've done. I'll draw such a

Move L.H. to D minor

por-trait of (a) man-y-clawed beast, and then if he scares me I'll

draw in a leash. I'll sketch a quick pic-ture or write a few

rit.
a tempo

lines and see tak-ing shape all the things in my mind.

rit.

StudyTime

This song has 3 parts: an **A section**, **B section**, and return of the **A section**.
Can you label each section in your music? Your teacher will help you.

D.C. al Fine

mf

rit.

pp

PRACTICE ____ TIMES DAILY AT A SLOW TEMPO.
PRACTICE ____ TIMES DAILY UP TO TEMPO.

★ ★ ★ ★ ★ ★ ★

Shade in a star for each day of practice.

Jig Along Home

Words and Music by
WOODY GUTHRIE

With spirit

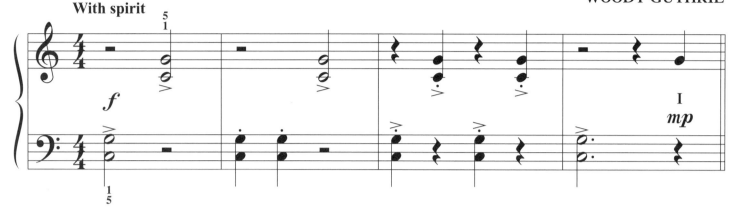

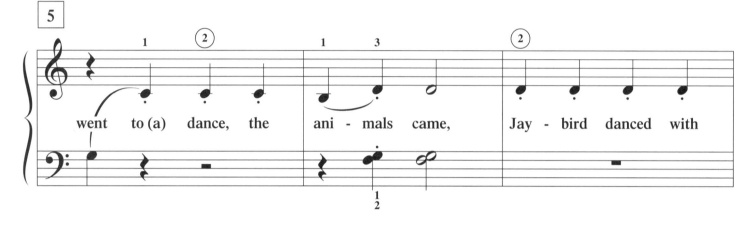

went to (a) dance, the ani - mals came, Jay - bird danced with

horse - shoes on, Grass - hopper danced till he fell on (the) floor,

Teacher Duet: (Student plays 1 octave higher)

R.H.

L.H.

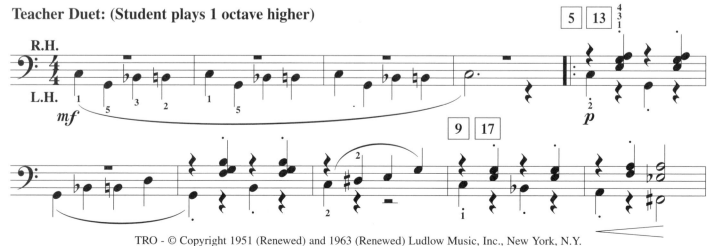

StudyTime

Tell your teacher what *crescendo* means.

Point out two places where the L.H. plays a *crescendo*.

22

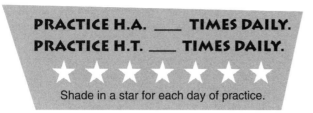

PRACTICE H.A. ____ TIMES DAILY.
PRACTICE H.T. ____ TIMES DAILY.
★ ★ ★ ★ ★ ★
Shade in a star for each day of practice.

The Bunny Hop

Words and Music by
RAY ANTHONY and
LEONARD AULETTI

Bright and bluesy, with a swing*

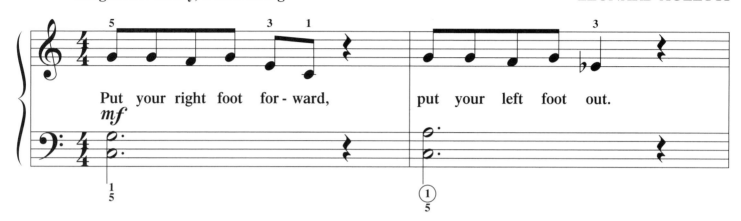

Put your right foot for-ward,   put your left foot out.

Do   the   Bun-ny   Hop,   now.   Hop,   hop,   hop!

*Note to Teacher: ♫ should be played in a long-short pattern (♫ = ♩³♪).

Teacher Duet: (Student plays 1 octave higher)

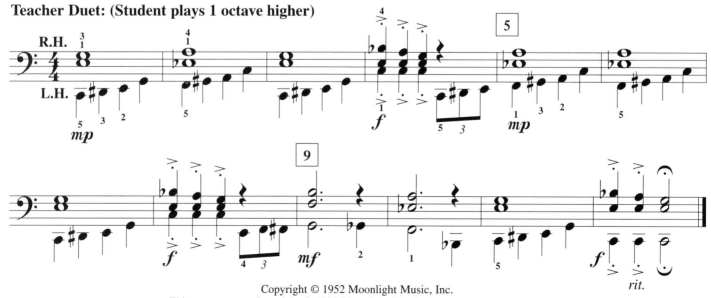

FF1040

5

Dance this new cre - a - tion, it's the new sen - sa - tion.

mf

Do the Bun - ny Hop, now. Hop, hop, hop!

f

9

Join in all the fun,_____ fa - ther, moth - er, son.

mf

Do the Bun - ny Hop, now. Hop, hop, hop!

rit.

f

StudyTime

Put a ✓ above each measure that has a rest on beat 4.

TOUR OF SONGLAND

Take a tour through SongLand by completing each example.

① Name the **sharp** in this "web-footed" melody. _____

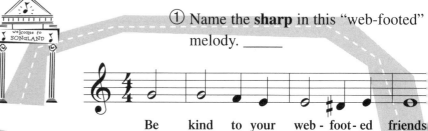

Be   kind   to   your   web - foot - ed   friends

② Stewball's melody begins on which beat? *1   2*   or   *3* (circle one)

Old   Stew - ball   was a   race - horse

③ Turn these quarter notes into "Hokey Pokey" 8th notes. Connect each group with a beam as shown in the example.

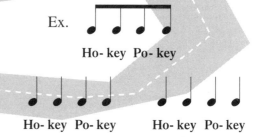

Ex.

Ho- key Po- key

Ho- key Po- key   Ho- key Po- key

④ Mail a "musical letter." Write one measure of your own $\frac{4}{4}$ rhythm on the envelope.

⑤ Write **1 2 3 4** under the correct beats for *Jig Along Home*.

Jig a- long, jig a- long,   jig a- long home.

⑥ Can you add to the list of "All the Things in My Piano"?

legs

piano lid

strings

⑦ Write the **time signature** for this *Bunny Hop* rhythm.

⑧ Draw a GIANT star on this page to show you have finished this book.